Pip's Peepers

These animals want to join in the fun too! Look out for them in every scene!

little mouse

cute guinea pig

lucky ladybird

buzzing bee

baby butterfly

nosy birds

A Trip with Pip

Where are you Pip?

The sun is shining and the weather is warm. It's the perfect day for a big day out. Pip's friends want to set out straight after breakfast. They hope that Pip is ready for the trip!

Pack up for Pip

Can you spot all of Pip's things?

Pip in the Pool

The swimming pool is packed today. Ooh!
The water is chilly! Big brave kitties take turns to
jump off the diving board. Little ones swim with
their armbands on. Pip wants to make a big splash.

Where are you Pip?

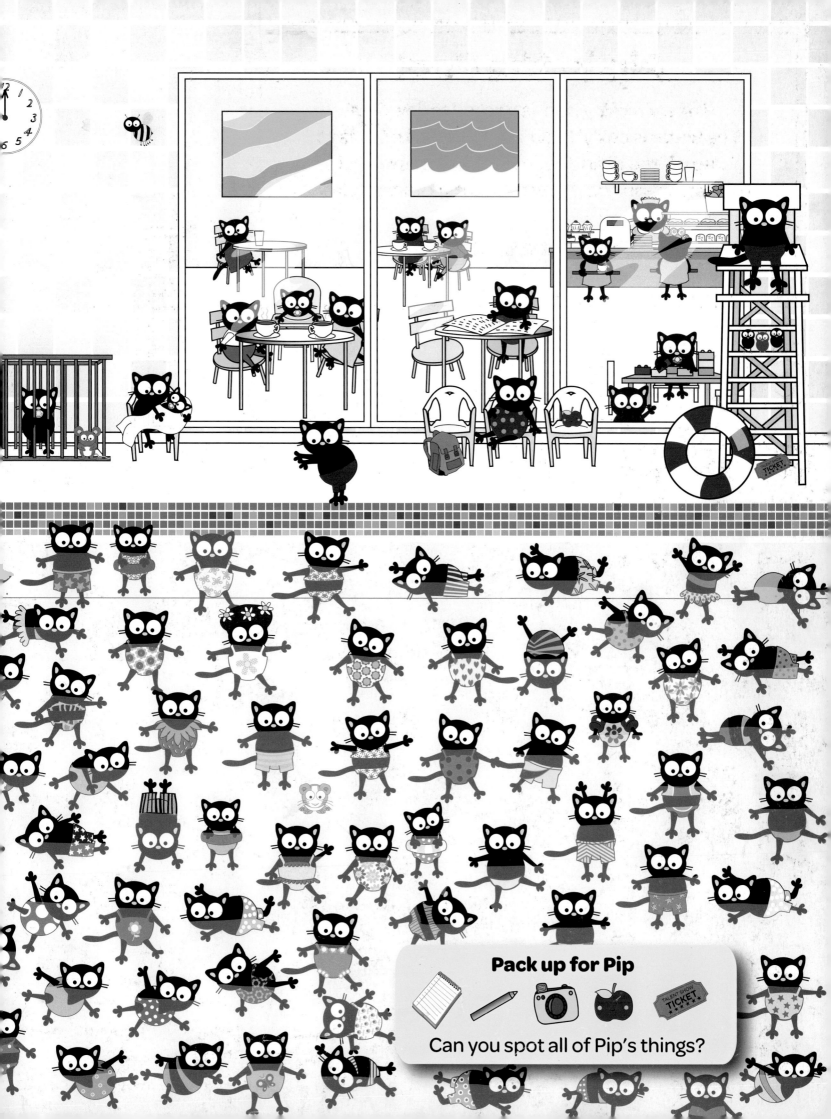

Pack up for Pip

Can you spot all of Pip's things?

V.I.Pip

Every kitty likes to be well-groomed!
Pip and the cats are booked in for some
five star pampering at the spa. Relaxing
mews-ic plays as the fancy felines
lick their paws and shine their whiskers.

Where are you Pip?

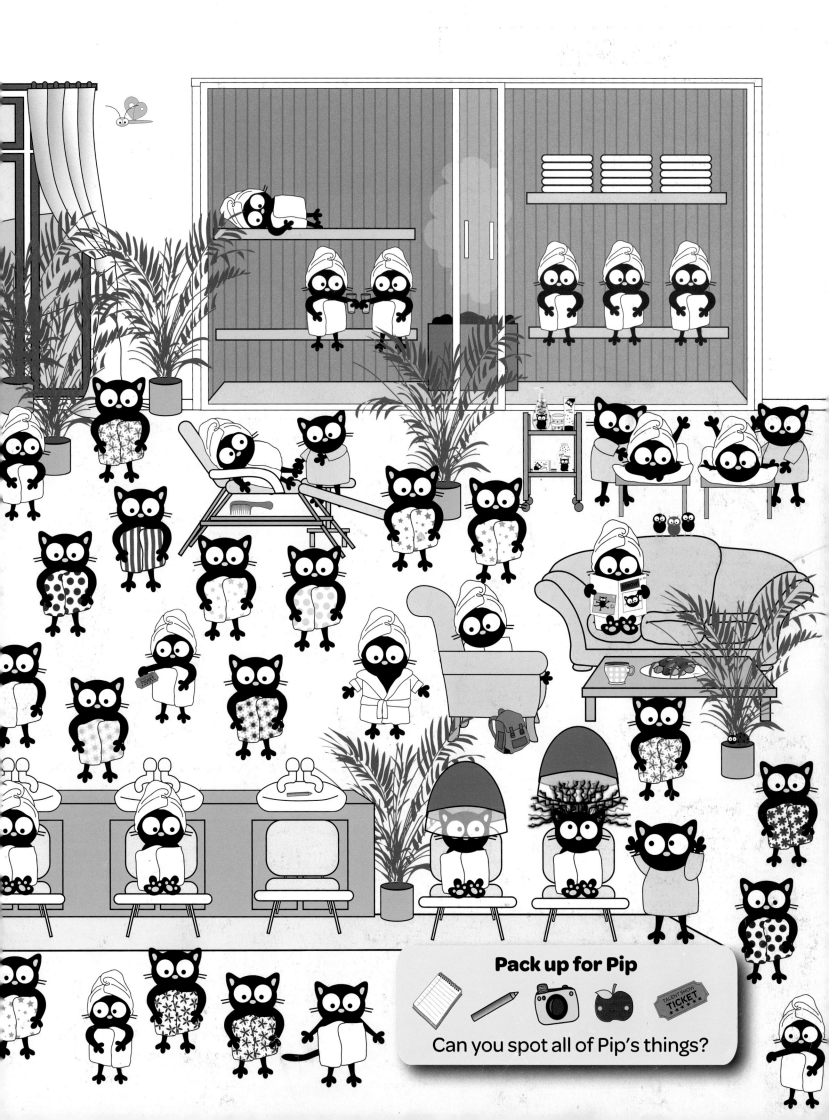

Pack up for Pip

Can you spot all of Pip's things?

Pip Pulls the Plug

Uh-oh! A careless kitty has left the tap running in the spa's hot tub! Foam has frothed out of the tub and over the sides.

7

5

2

1

3

6

4

8

A FAIRY TALE

Can you help Pip pull the plug and put things right again? Draw a line to match the bubbly shapes with the objects hidden underneath them.

A

D

A FAIRY TALE

G

B

E

C

F

H

A Plate for Pip

It's time for the happy cats to head outside for a sunshine lunch. This fancy fish restaurant is purrfect! Waiters wander up and down, handing out smoked kippers. Over lunch, Pip's pals chatter about the Town Talent Show.

Where are you Pip?

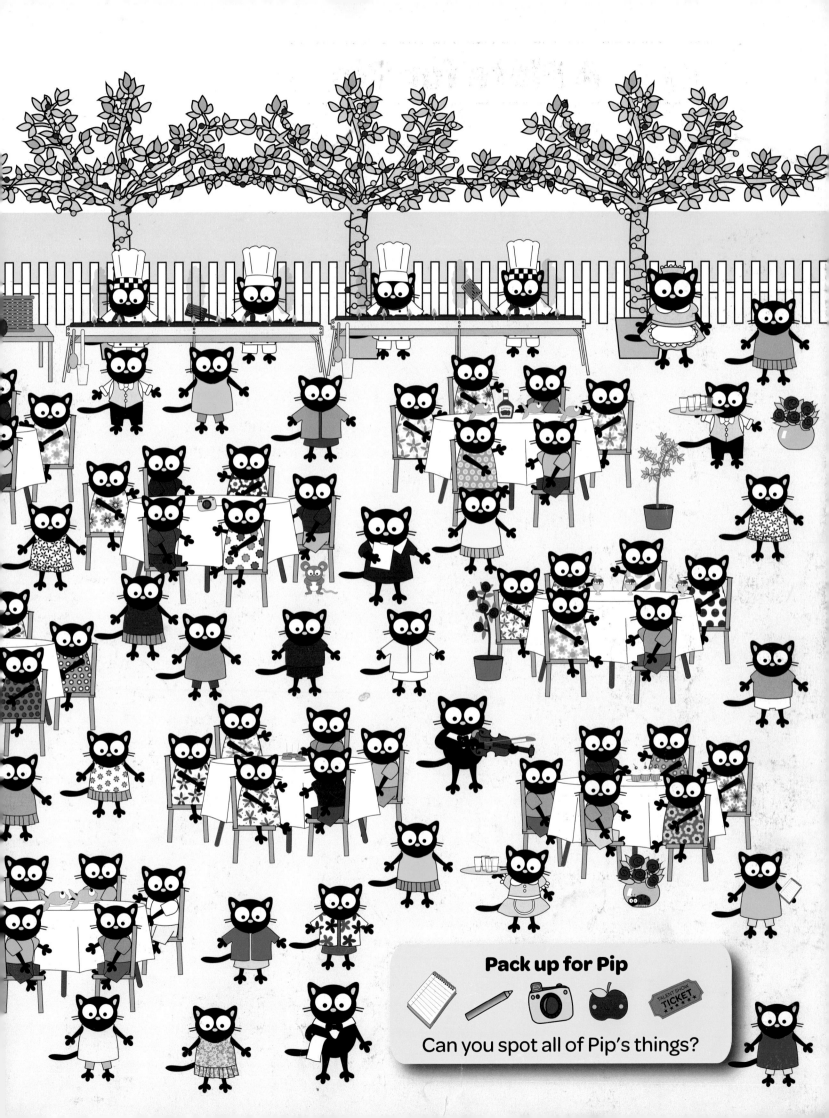

Pack up for Pip

Can you spot all of Pip's things?

Pip at the Palace

The palace is the grandest place Pip has ever visited!
The curious kitties have come to explore the royal gardens.
Pip skips away to look at the sparkling fountain
with its pretty princess statue.

Where are you Pip?

To the maze

Pack up for Pip

TICKET

Can you spot all of Pip's things?

Pip's Maze

Pip has wandered into the palace's famous maze.
The little cat can only spot hedges in every direction.
Can you help Pip get out?

Pip

Lost kitties should go back to the centre of the maze. If you always stick to the left hand side, the path will lead you ou

Pip at the Petting Farm

Pip's special day out is getting better and better!
The friends have popped into the petting farm
to say hello to the cute furry animals. Nibbly
hamsters, floppy-eared rabbits and squeaky
guinea-pigs – Pip loves them all.

Where are you Pip?

Pack up for Pip

Can you spot all of Pip's things?

Pip at the Shops

No day trip is complete without visiting the shops. Look at all the feline fashion! Stylish kitties browse up the aisles, slurping smoothies as they window shop. Pip hopes to pick up a bargain or two.

Where are you Pip?

Paws For Tea

CA

SWIMPLES

CAT FACE

BANANA BAG PUSS PUSS IN BOOTS

Mew Shoe CAT MAN DO Paws 'R' Us

Pack up for Pip

Can you spot all of Pip's things?

Pip's Puzzle

Pip has had a super-successful shop! The clever cat picked out all sorts of dressing-up clothes.

What did the kitty buy? Look at each of the items on Pip's shopping list. Now draw a circle around the picture that matches it best.

1. A new hat to wear at a wedding.

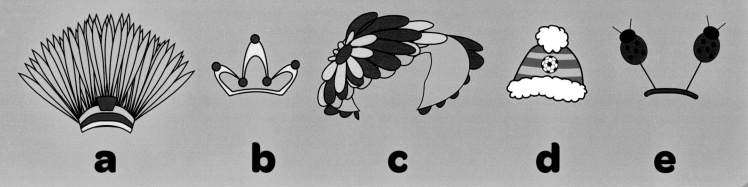

a   b   c   d   e

2. A smart pair of riding boots.

a   b   c   d   e

3. A dapper new suit for driving.

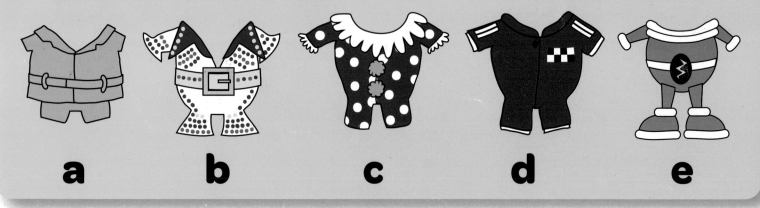

a   b   c   d   e

4. A pretty new ballet outfit.

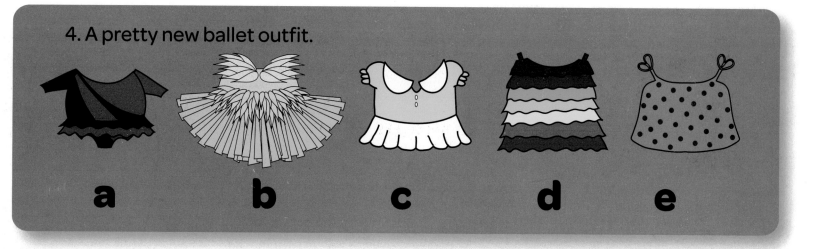

a   b   c   d   e

5. A pair of red party shoes.

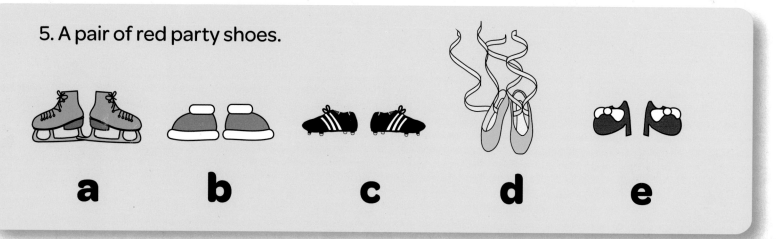

a   b   c   d   e

6. A shirt for wearing on the farm.

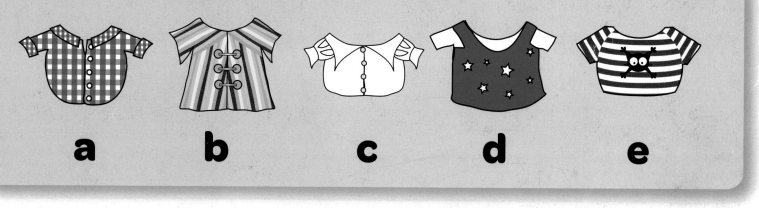

a   b   c   d   e

Answers 1C, 2D, 3D, 4B, 5E, 6A

Pip's Top Ticket

Town Talent Show

The crazy cats top off their day with a walk to the park – they can't wait to find out who's won the Town Talent Show! Excited kitties unfold their chairs and curl up on rugs. Pip wanders through the crowds in excitement.

Where are you Pip?

PRESS

Pack up for Pip

Can you spot all of Pip's things?

TICKET

A Prize Party for Pip!

Who'd have thought that Pip would be presented with the kitty crown in the Town Talent Show? The puzzled pussycat decides to celebrate with the other copy-kitties.

Where are you Pip?

Pack up for Pip

Can you spot all of Pip's things?

Put Pip in the Picture

Why do you think Pip won top prize in the Town Talent Show?
Take a look back at the kitty's crazy day out.

Pip teed off the trip with some kitty juggling.

Then the kitty made a splash in the pool.

At the spa, Pip made lots of funny faces.

Over lunch the kitty made all the guests giggle and gawp.

Pip almost got wet all over again
in the palace gardens!

Pip was full of smiley surprises
at the petting farm.

The kitty had a smashing time
at the fun fair.

A stop at the shops proved
that Pip will give anything a try.

Everyone loves to laugh at Pip!

Pip the cat is the biggest star in town!

There's Pip!

Pip is a star, but you are a hero! Pip has had lots of hide-and-seek adventures, but has still made it home safe and sound. Thank you for finding the kitty.

Happy to keep hunting?

There are still a few more things to spot in the busy pages of this book. Flick back through Pip's day out. Can you track down all ten objects? Put a big tick next to each one you find.

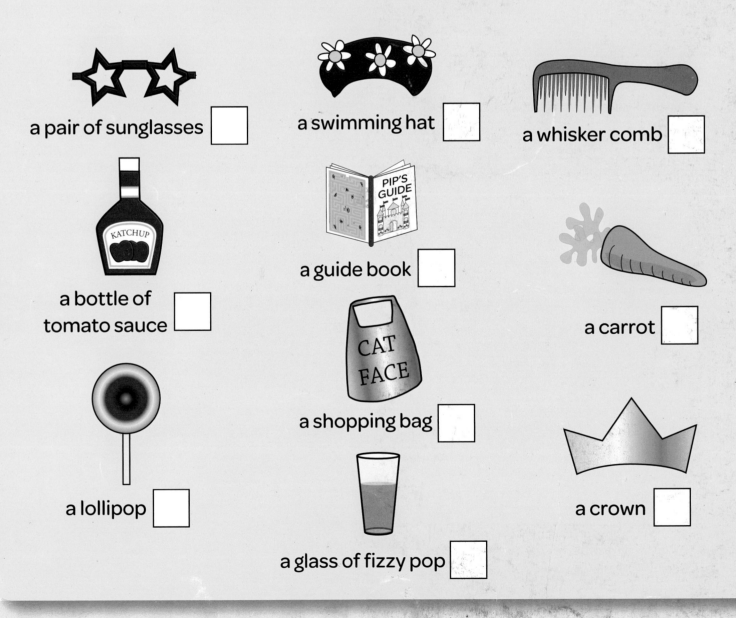

a pair of sunglasses ☐

a swimming hat ☐

a whisker comb ☐

a bottle of tomato sauce ☐

a guide book ☐

a carrot ☐

a lollipop ☐

a shopping bag ☐

a crown ☐

a glass of fizzy pop ☐